The Madam & Eve Coll

By S. Francis, H. Dugmore & Ri

David Philip Publishers
Cape Town

First published in 1993 by Weekly Mail & Guardian Publishing

Published in 1999 by David Philip Publishers (Pty) Ltd,
208 Werdmuller Centre, Newry Street, Claremont 7708, Cape Town, South Africa

First edition 1993
Second impression 1993
Second edition 1999

Pre-Foreword Introduction

This isn't a foreword, because that's already been done. This is an introduction that comes before the foreword, sort of a pre-foreword foreword. But, on the other hand, because the original foreword was written seven years ago, technically it's not a pre-foreword but a post-foreword.

That's the kind of problem you have when you're reprinting a book that's been out of print for a long time. Every year, a few months before the Christmas holidays, we've published a Madam & Eve annual, a collection of the year's best strips. Every year, we have our annual 'book tour' to promote sales, do interviews and sign books ... and every year, wherever we go, we're always asked the same three questions:

1. *'Where do you get your ideas?'*
(From a small shop in Bloemfontein.)
2. *'Do you think that South Africans are finally learning to laugh at themselves?'*
(Yes. However, for many years, the rest of the world weren't in on the joke.)
And finally, we're always asked
3. *'Where can we get a copy of your first book?'*

Ah, yes. Our *first* book.
It was back in 1993 – and we decided to print the book ourselves, in partnership with the first newspaper ever to run Madam & Eve, the *Weekly Mail*. Working together, we did everything. We built our own in-store displays.

We helped with the marketing, publicity, distribution and delivery. And then we hoped that someone would actually buy it.

To our very great surprise, some people did. In the next six months, during the hype and excitement of the country's first democratic election, The *Madam & Eve Collection* quietly sold out, becoming that year's number one paperback. Round about then, the question 'Where can we get a copy of your first book?' was first asked. All the subsequent Madam & Eve annuals have gone into reprints – and most of them are still available in a bookstore near you. But *number uno* – not a chance. Even we didn't have any copies left!

Until now.

We've always wanted to say this, so here goes: **By popular demand, here, once again, available in bookstores everywhere, is our very first book** – *The Madam & Eve Collection* – **as it first appeared way back in those heady days of 1993.**

Enjoy!

Stephen Francis
Harry Dugmore
Rico Schacherl

Foreword

Hello. My name is Gus Silber, and I'd like to ... hey! Do you mind? I'm trying to write a foreword here! How do you think I'm ever going to get it done if you keep rushing past the foreword to get to the cartoons?

Yes, I know it's Madam and Eve, the hip and penetrating series about a white South African madam and her, well, her – help me out here, guys, I don't want to get this politically incorrect – her Domestic Maintenance co-ordinator. Thanks.

I know, also, that it's the most popular contemporary satirical series ever maid – whoops – MADE in South Africa, and that you don't want to let anything as irrelevant as a foreword stand in the way of your enjoyment of this official debut Madam and Eve cartoon collection.

I know in this age of the rapidly diminishing attention-span, that um, that ... where was I again? That very few people even bother to read forewords anymore, which is not particularly surprising when you consider how poorly people get paid for writing them.

But let me stress, I am not writing this foreword for the money I would be getting if I were being paid for writing this foreword. I am writing it because I sincerely believe that I have something important to say about the meaning of Madam and Eve in our changing South African society, and it is with this in mind that I would like to explore the social and political subtext that lies just beneath the ... pardon?

Oh. Thanks, Eve. A cup of tea would be nice. White, no sugar. And one Lemon Meringue biscuit. No, make that two. Thanks. Now, as I was saying, when we take a closer look at the everyday working relationship of Madam and Eve in the context of ... in the context of ... NOW WHAT?

Oh, hi, Steve. Yes, I'm getting to it now. Of course I haven't forgotten. Yes, I know people haven't got all day to wade through the foreword. Yes I do realise how important it is to say a few words about the guys who actually produce the series in the first place. OKAY, ALL RIGHT! IT'S NOT AS IF I'M GETTING PAID TO DO THIS, OR ANYTHING!

Boy. Some people. That was S Francis of the Madam and Eve team on the line. He's the guy who does the plots and stuff, and he has asked me to say a few words about S Francis, his co-writer H Dugmore, and R Schacherl, the guy who does the drawings. Of course. I was getting to that. Hand me that piece of paper with the words on, Steve. Okay. "Comic genius." "Scalpel-sharp satire." "A powerhouse creative team with their finger on the panic-button of contemporary South African society." "Buy this book." "Get one for your Domestic Maintenance co-ordinator or Madam too." "Hurry up and finish the foreword."

Hello? Hello? Hey, where is everybody? Am I talking to the wall, or what? Where's my tea? Eve? Eve? Okay, I give up. I'm going to check out some cartoons. I mean this is *Madam and Eve* we're talking about. See you there. And don't forget to read this when you're finished, okay?

Gus Silber

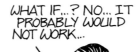

STICK 'EM UP.

MADAM!! IT'S FOR YOU!

HI. JOHN JACKSON... "**FIRST STRIKE SECURITY**". SORRY IF I SCARED YOU, BUT I HAD TO DEMONSTRATE HOW PITIFULLY VULNERABLE YOU ARE WITHOUT A GOOD **SECURITY SYSTEM**.

I SEE YOUR MAID WANTS TO KILL ME RIGHT NOW. IT'S A **COMMON** REACTION. HERE... HAVE A BROCHURE.

YOU'VE HEARD OF "**ARMED RESPONSE**", RIGHT? WE'LL, WE OFFER A DELUXE VERSION...

"**ARMED NUCLEAR RESPONSE!**"

...ARMED NUCLEAR RESPONSE?

YES. SOMEONE TRIPS THE SILENT ALARM AND WE **NUKE** YOUR HOUSE FROM AN AERIAL ATTACK. WIPES OUT ALL CRIMINALS AT **GROUND ZERO.**

NUKE MY HOUSE?

HEY... WE'RE VERY **ACCURATE.**

SLAM!

WUP! WUP! WUP! WUP!

SALES LEADER TO CHOPPER ONE. CANCEL THE **FREE DEMONSTRATION.**

MADAM & Eve

BY S. FRANCIS, H. DUGMORE & RICO

SO... YOU'RE EVE'S NEW **BOYFRIEND.**

...WHILE I'M WAITING FOR EVE TO GET READY, DO YOU MIND IF I USE YOUR BATHROOM?

ER, OF COURSE.

UH, I THINK I CAN **FIND** IT BY MYSELF...

SURE THING... JUST GO **PAST** THE **TV** AND **VIDEO-MACHINE**...WHICH NO ONE IN THEIR RIGHT MIND WOULD WANT TO **STEAL** BECAUSE THEY'RE BOTH BROKEN!

...THEN TURN RIGHT AT ONE OF THE MANY **ARMED RESPONSE BUTTONS** CONVENIENTLY LOCATED THROUGHOUT THE HOUSE...

...THEN GO BY THE DOOR TO MY BEDROOM...WHERE I KEEP MY **WORTH-LESS** IMITATION COSTUME JEWELLERY AND WHERE OUR **VICIOUS ROTTWEILER** SLEEPS...

© RAPID PHASE PRODUCTIONS 1992

HI. I'M READY... WHERE'S SOL?

HE'LL BE RIGHT BACK.

...BY THE WAY...WHAT DOES YOUR BOYFRIEND DO FOR A **LIVING**..?

HE STEALS **TOILET SEATS.** WHY?

I JUST LOVE WORKING FOR SOMEONE SO GULLIBLE...

14

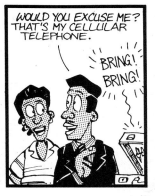

MADAM & EVE

BY S. FRANCIS, H. DUGMORE & RICO

THIS IS RIDICULOUS! A **SANGOMA** IN A THREE PIECE SUIT, WITH A CELLULAR PHONE AND A LAP-TOP COMPUTER.

BUT MADAM...IT'S NOT HIS APPEARANCE THAT COUNTS... IT'S HIS **SPIRITUAL** POWER!

CLAC CLIC CLIC CLIC

...GO AHEAD, EVE. PUSH THE "B" BUTTON ON THE COMPUTER AND WE'LL **ELECTRONICALLY** ROLL THE BONES.

HMMM. A VERY INTERESTING GROUPING.

BEEP. BEEP. BEEP.

EVE, I CAN'T **BELIEVE** YOU'RE BEING TAKEN IN BY THIS GUY... BY THE WAY, IS THAT YOUR **BMW** IN THE DRIVEWAY?

YES. WHY?

...IT LOOKS LIKE SOMEONE IS TRYING TO **STEAL** YOUR CAR.

HMM. HE OBVIOUSLY DIDN'T SEE MY "SANGOMA STICKER" ON THE BUMPER...

CLIC. CLIC. CLIC. CLAC. CLIC

I'D BE A LITTLE MORE CONCERNED IF I WERE YOU. HE'S JUST OPENED YOUR DOOR!

TRUST ME. IT'S **NO PROBLEM.**

:GASP!: HE JUST TURNED INTO A **FROG**!

POOF!

YES. A **CRUDE** SPELL ...BUT A LOT MORE EFFECTIVE THAN A CAR ALARM.

NOW... WHERE WERE WE...?

~RIBBIT!

WAIT! DO YOU TAKE CREDIT CARDS?!

©Rapid Phase Entertainment 1992

18

19

MADAM! MADAM!

I'M TALKING TO YOU FROM **HEAVEN**... THIS IS **YOU KNOW WHO!**

UH, OH. I'M IN FOR IT NOW.

WAIT A MINUTE... YOUR VOICE! YOU'RE A **WOMAN**?

YES.

...INCIDENTALLY, I'M ALSO **BLACK**.

AND I HAVE CHOSEN **YOU**.

ME?

YES. TO SPREAD THE MESSAGE OF **PEACE** AND **COMPASSION** THROUGHOUT SOUTH AFRICA.

BUT... THAT'S SUCH A BIG JOB! WHERE... HOW DO I POSSIBLY START?

WELL, FIRST, YOU COULD START BY GIVING YOUR **MAID** AN **INCREASE** OF TEN RAND A DAY.

IN FACT, BETTER MAKE IT **TWENTY**.

...AND HER **LONG** WORKING HOURS LEAVE MUCH TO BE DESIRED...

HEY!!

CLICK!

I'M EVE SISULU, HERE NOW, THE NEWS. TODAY'S TOP HEADLINE... "HEARTLESS MADAM LOCKS MAID IN BROOM CLOSET"...MORE TO FOLLOW...

BY S.FRANCIS, H.DUGMORE & RICO

© 1992 Rapid Phase Productions

20

MADAM & Eve

BY S. FRANCIS, H. DUGMORE & RICO.

MADAM, I'VE GOT TO TAKE A FEW DAYS LEAVE. MY UNCLE JOE JUST PASSED AWAY.

OH, I'M SORRY TO HEAR THAT. I FEEL BAD FOR YOUR UNCLE JOE...

...HE'S ALREADY DIED **THREE** TIMES!

WHAT?

I'VE GOT IT ALL RIGHT HERE. I'VE BEEN KEEPING TRACK OF ALL YOUR "EMERGENCY LEAVE."

ACCORDING TO THIS, YOUR "UNCLE JOE" PASSED AWAY IN **AUGUST '88,** IN **SEPTEMBER '90** AND **JULY OF THIS YEAR!**

AND LET'S NOT FORGET YOUR SISTER ... SHE FELL OFF A BUILDING **THREE** YEARS AGO, HAD A HEART ATTACK **TWO** YEARS AGO AND A BRAIN TUMOR LAST **OCTOBER.**

WELL, WHAT HAVE YOU GOT TO SAY FOR YOURSELF?

© Rapid Phase Entertainment 1992

I THOUGHT SO.

THE DISHES ARE IN THE SINK.

DID YOU EVER THINK THAT IF I HAD A BIT MORE LEAVE, MY FAMILY WOULDN'T DIE OFF SO OFTEN?!

MADAM & Eve

BY S. FRANCIS, H. DUGMORE & RICO.

LOOK AT THIS! THERE'S NOTHING BUT **RUGBY** ON TV ALL DAY!

ACTUALLY, I HAPPEN TO **LIKE** RUGBY...

...IT'S THE ONLY TIME I CAN WATCH **THIRTY WHITE GUYS** BEAT EACH OTHER SENSELESS...

HEY... YOU'RE RIGHT, EVE! HOW COME THERE'S NO **BLACK** RUGBY PLAYERS?

YOU MEAN, ...YOU DON'T **KNOW**?

IT'S THE RUGBY BALL. THE **TRUTH** IS, BLACK PEOPLE ARE **ALLERGIC** TO LEATHER.

NO!

YES, IT'S ONE OF OUR **WEAKNESSES**... MAKES US BREAK OUT IN RASHES. LET ME TELL YOU... THERE'S A LOT OF **SECRET** THINGS YOU WHITE PEOPLE DON'T KNOW ABOUT US!

REALLY?! LIKE WHAT? ...TELL ME!

FOR EXAMPLE, WHEN WE'RE RIDING IN A **LIFT** WITH YOU AND YOU CAN'T **UNDERSTAND** US BECAUSE WE'RE TALKING OUR OWN LANGUAGE?... WE'RE USUALLY SAYING BAD THINGS ABOUT **YOU**.

I **THOUGHT** SO! GO ON...

AND, WHENEVER YOU GO ON **VACATION**, WE CALL UP ALL OUR FRIENDS, INVITE THEM OVER TO YOUR HOUSE, USE YOUR **BATHROOM** AND TRY ON ALL YOUR **CLOTHES**!

I SUSPECTED THAT! **MORE!** TELL ME MORE!

© Rapid Phase Production 1992

SORRY. I CAN'T. I'M SWORN TO **SECRECY**.

PLEASE?! I'LL GIVE YOU WHATEVER YOU WANT! I'LL **PAY** YOU!!

OKAY. IF YOU **INSIST**... BUT GET US A COUPLE OF COFFEES. THIS COULD TAKE A WHILE.

...BE RIGHT BACK

SOMETIMES I JUST CAN'T HELP MYSELF...

MADAM & Eve

BY S. FRANCIS, H. DUGMORE & RICO

ERIC... DO WE **REALLY** HAVE TO WATCH YOUR DOCUMENTARY FOR FILM SCHOOL?

TRUST ME, MOM... YOU'LL LOVE IT! AFTER ALL, **YOU TWO** ARE THE **STARS.**

I CALL IT "**THE MADAM FROM HELL.**" WHAT DO YOU THINK?

I THINK YOU CAN KISS YOUR TRUST FUND GOOD BYE.

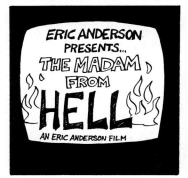

ERIC ANDERSON PRESENTS... THE MADAM FROM HELL

AN ERIC ANDERSON FILM

"... SOUTH AFRICA... LAND OF BEAUTY AND CONTRAST...."

"AND EVERY DAY A BATTLE RAGES..., A BATTLE OF WILLS... BETWEEN AN UNDERPAID MAID....."

ERIC! GET THAT CAMERA OUT OF MY FACE!!

"... AND HER HEARTLESS, CRUEL MADAM... "

ERIC! FOR PETE'S SAKE! I'M TAKING A SHOWER!!

"WHILE EVE, THE LOWLY SERVANT, IS **EXPLOITED...**"

...ERIC!

"... THE MADAM RELAXES IN THE **LAP OF LUXURY** WITH FINE JEWELLERY AND CLOTHES...."

ERIC!! GET OUT OF HERE! I'M DRESSING!!

"WILL BLACK AND WHITE PEOPLE IN SOUTH AFRICA EVER RESOLVE THEIR DIFFERENCES AND LIVE TOGETHER IN HARMONY...?"

"... OR WILL THEY BE KILLED BY **GIANT FLESH-EATING DINOSAURS?**"

GIANT, FLESH-EATING DINOSAURS?

HEY—I THOUGHT IT NEEDED A TOUCH OF **SPIELBERG.**

ADAM & Eve

EVE! DON'T TELL ME YOU HAVEN'T FINISHED **CLEANING** THE GARDEN OF EDEN YET?

WAIT TILL HE FINDS OUT THAT THE LEAF HE'S WEARING IS **POISON IVY.**

SADDAM & Eve

EVE! HURRY UP WITH MY SHIRT! I'M INVADING KUWAIT TODAY!

...THE MOTHER OF ALL COMPLAINERS.

ADAM & Steve

HEY **STEVE**...HURRY UP! BY THE TIME YOU **FINISH** WITH MY SHIRT, IT'LL BE TOO LATE TO CRUISE THE BARS.

BITCH. BITCH. BITCH.

MADONNA & Eve

HEY **EVE**!...ISN'T IT GREAT TO BE **NAKED**!? IT FEELS SO FREE! ...NO HANG-UPS! ...NO HASSLES!

...NO **IRONING.**

© Rapid Phase Entertainment 1992

HERE WE ARE, EVE. HOME AT LAST...**WHAT THE !!?**

♪ ♪...LIKE A VIRGIN...

SEE WHAT HAPPENS WHEN WE TAKE A **VACATION !!**

WHO'S MADONNA?

BY S. FRANCIS, H. DUGMORE & RICO

MADAM

AAAAAAAAAAAH!

BY S.FRANCIS, H.DUGMORE & RICO.

...PARKTOWN PRAWNS?

IN THE KITCHEN!!

LOOK AT THEM. THEY'RE **HORRIBLE**!!

GOOD--THEY'VE SPOTTED US.

QUICK EVE ...USE THE **BUG-SPRAY**

...GET READY.

PFFFFFT!!

WOW... EXCELLENT...

OKAY--NOW HOLD IT IN FOR AS LONG AS YOU CAN.

...THEY'RE STILL **ALIVE**!

INCREDIBLE! I THINK THEY ACTUALLY **LIKE** IT!

FAR OUT...

HERE--**SMASH** 'EM WITH THIS **HAMMER**!

MADAM...THIS ISN'T EXACTLY PART OF MY JOB DESCRIPTION.

HURRY UP!

THWACK!!

DID YOU JUST FEEL A SLIGHT BREEZE?

NO. DID YOU?

MADAM...WE CAN'T STAY IN THE BATHROOM FOREVER.

IS THE TOWEL STILL UNDER THE DOOR?!

MADAM & EVE

BY S. FRANCIS, H. DUGMORE & RICO

TONIGHT, OUR GUEST IS A MAN WHO'S PROUD TO TALK ABOUT HIS ASSOCIATION WITH THE **DIRECTORATE OF COVERT COLLECTION.**

THAT'S RIGHT, JOHN. I HAVE ABSOLUTELY **NOTHING** TO HIDE.

SO. WHAT'S YOUR NAME?

CALL ME "MISTER X".

...TELL US, "MISTER X"... WHAT ABOUT THE NUMEROUS "DIRTY TRICKS" YOU'VE BEEN ACCUSED OF?...

FIRST OF ALL, JOHN, I WOULDN'T CALL THEM "DIRTY TRICKS"...

WHAT WOULD YOU CALL THEM?

PRACTICAL JOKES.

PRACTICAL JOKES!?

YES... MERELY TO IRRITATE AND HARMLESSLY ANNOY ENEMIES OF THE STATE.

UNBELIEVABLE!! ARE YOU SAYING THIS IS ALL **HARMLESS FUN!?**

THAT'S ALL IT IS, JOHN... ITCHING POWDER... HAND-BUZZERS... SENDING A DOZEN ANCHOVY PIZZAS TO BISHOP TUTU... STUFF LIKE THAT.

THIS IS **OUTRAGEOUS!!** YOU'RE TELLING US THAT IS THE **WORST** YOU'VE EVER DONE!?

WELL, NO.

AHA!

ONE TIME WE BROKE INTO CHRIS HANI'S HOUSE AND **SHORT-SHEETED** ALL THE BEDS.

RUBBISH! I'M NOT BUYING ANY OF THIS!!

CALM DOWN, JOHN. SIT BACK AND RELAX.

©Rapid Phase Entertainment 1992

WE'LL BE RIGHT BACK AFTER... *BAAARRRP!!* WHAT THE...!!?

WHOOPEE CUSHION, JOHN. ONE OF OUR FAVOURITES.

THINGS TO DO TODAY

Give Eve a big RAISE

THERE'S NOTHING LIKE SOMETHING **FUNNY** TO START YOUR DAY.

AS CHAIRPERSON OF OUR NEIGHBOURHOOD MAID'S GROUP, I SAY... IT'S TIME TO **STRIKE FOR MORE MONEY!**

YES! LET'S DO IT!

ALRIGHT!

EXCUSE ME... BUT "LOVING" STARTS IN FIVE MINUTES.

YES! LET'S DO IT! ALRIGHT! HURRY!

NEVER SCHEDULE THE STRUGGLE DURING A GOOD SOAP OPERA.

SINCE YOU WON'T GIVE ME A **RAISE**, MADAM, I'M GOING ON **STRIKE!** AS OF NOW I'M OFFICIALLY ON **STAY-AWAY!**

FINE! YOU THINK I NEED **YOU**?! I'LL JUST DO ALL THE CLEANING AND COOKING **MYSELF!**

BEFORE YOU GO... JUST ANSWER ME ONE QUESTION...

WHICH IS THE STOVE AND WHICH IS THE DISHWASHER?

MADAM & EVE

BY S. FRANCIS, H. DUGMORE & RICO

MOM! HAVE YOU SEEN THAT NEW BOOK MY FRIEND SENT ME FROM OVERSEAS?!

THE ONE BY MADONNA!?

SEX

OFFICER... AS A **MORALLY-MINDED**, LAW-ABIDING CITIZEN, I WISH TO TURN OVER TO YOU THIS **BANNED** PUBLICATION....

WANTED

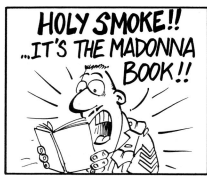

HOLY SMOKE!! ...IT'S THE MADONNA BOOK!!

GUYS! THE MADONNA BOOK!...WE GOT A COPY!

WANTED

OH YEAH...WE'LL DEFINITELY HAVE TO **CONFISCATE** THIS.

CAN I CONFISCATE IT AFTER YOU?

WOAH! CHECK OUT THIS ONE!

HOW DOES SHE DO THAT!?

HEY!... MOVE YOUR THUMB!

CENSORSHIP... IT'S A TOUGH JOB, BUT SOMEONE'S GOT TO DO IT.

HEY! WHERE'S THE KEY TO THE XEROX MACHINE?!

© Rapid Phase Entertainment 1992

MADAM & Eve

BY S. FRANCIS, H. DUGMORE & RICO.

MADAM...THANK YOU FOR INVITING ME TO THE OPENING OF THE **LOST CITY.**

DON'T THANK ME. THIS IS AN IMPORTANT EVENT IN SOUTH AFRICAN HISTORY. IT'S A MAGNIFICENT ATTRACTION... RICH IN ANCIENT CULTURE AND INNOVATIVE DESIGN...

WHAT DO YOU WANT TO SEE FIRST?

THE SLOT MACHINES.

LOOK EVE!... EVEN THE EMPLOYEES WEAR **SPECIAL COSTUMES.** ISN'T IT THRILLING?!

WELCOME TO SOL KERZNER'S LOST CITY. A MAGICAL AND REALISTIC WORLD, CONCEIVED WITH TASTE, SPLENDOR AND BEAUTY.

WE'RE LOOKING FOR THE **SLOT MACHINES.**

TURN RIGHT BY THE LINE OF PHONY ELEPHANTS, THEN GO LEFT BY THE GIANT FAKE ROCK AND FOLLOW THE IMMITATION GOLD COLUMNS.

LATER...

EVE!... WE'RE GOING IN **CIRCLES!** THIS IS THE THIRD TIME WE'VE SEEN THE **SOL KERZNER COMMEMORATIVE STATUE.**

EXCUSE ME... WE'RE LOST. DO YOU KNOW WHERE THE SLOT MACHINES ARE?

NO...I DON'T.

ALTHOUGH I DON'T APPROVE OF GAMBLING, I BELIEVE IT IS THE RIGHT OF THE INDIVIDUAL TO DETERMINE WHAT IS RIGHT OR WRONG...ESPECIALLY, IF WE ARE TO LIVE IN A WORLD OF PEACE, HARMONY AND UNDERSTANDING. THANK YOU.

... A **MISS WORLD** CONTESTANT.

DEFINITELY.

MADAM & Eve

BY S.FRANCIS, H.DUGMORE & RICO

MADAM! COME QUICK! THERE'S A STRANGE MAN IN THE HOUSE!

HOLLYWOOD SID!? ...FROM "DOONESBURY"?

MADAM! EVE.!... WHO LOVES YA, BABE?

"DOONESBURY"? I THOUGHT YOU PEOPLE HANG OUT NEAR THE BACK OF THE NEWSPAPER?

EVE. BABE. WE'RE **SYNDICATED**. WE CAN HANG OUT WHEREVER WE WANT!

IT'S TIME FOR YOU TO **THINK BIG**, LADIES. LET ME BE YOUR MANAGER. WE'RE TALKING MADAM & EVE **T-SHIRTS**, MADAM & EVE **LUNCH-BOXES**...MAYBE EVEN A MADAM & EVE **TV-SERIES**!!

...OF COURSE, THEY'D WANT A FEW CHANGES...WE MAKE MADAM "BLACK"...AND EVE "WHITE". KIND OF A "**TRADING PLACES**" THING.

I'VE ALREADY MADE SOME INQUIRIES...I HEAR **MERYL STREEP** AND **WHITNEY HOUSTON** ARE VERY INTERESTED...

FORGET IT, EVE AND I ARE...

DID YOU SAY **WHITNEY HOUSTON**!?

...CALLED HER ON THE CAR-PHONE YESTERDAY!

EVE!

SORRY, WE'RE NOT IN-TERESTED.

...I **THOUGHT** THIS MIGHT BE A **TOUGH** NEGOTIATION...SO I BROUGHT SOMEONE TO HELP ME CONVINCE YOU...

© Rapid Phase Entertainment 1992

ZONKER!?

HEY LADIES!

IT'S GOOD TO BE HERE IN SUNNY SOUTH AFRICA ...BY THE WAY... WHAT EXACTLY IS "**DAGGA**"?

ZONKER!

MADAM & Eve

BY S. FRANCIS, H.L. DUGMORE & RICO

MADAM... I'M BEGGING YOU! PLEASE DON'T DO THIS!

SORRY, EVE! BUT I WANT TO TRULY EXPERIENCE WHAT IT MEANS TO BE A BLACK WOMAN IN SOUTH AFRICA!

WELL?... HOW DO I LOOK?

...YOU'VE GOT SHOE POLISH ON YOUR COLLAR.

MADAM... COME BACK!

HOW CAN I UNDERSTAND THE PLIGHT OF YOUR PEOPLE... UNLESS I WALK IN YOUR SHOES?!

A WHOLE NEW WORLD AND CULTURE COULD OPEN UP TO ME!

...BUT, MADAM.

I CAN WALK AMONG YOU UNDETECTED... MAYBE EVEN WRITE A NEWSPAPER ARTICLE! INVESTIGATIVE UNDERCOVER JOURNALISM!

BUT MADAM -- YOU DON'T EVEN SPEAK THE LANGUAGE!

A MINOR DETAIL!

MADAM—PLEASE LET'S GO BACK INSIDE THE HOUSE.

WAIT! THE ULTIMATE TEST! HERE COMES SOMEBODY!

© Rapid Phase Entertainment 1993

LOOK AT THAT! SOME CRAZY WHITE WOMAN WITH SHOE POLISH ON HER FACE.

MUST BE SOME KIND OF NEW LIBERAL FAD.

SEE? I TOLD YOU IT WOULD WORK! NOW LET'S GO SOMEWHERE WHERE I CAN BE EXPLOITED!

MADAM & Eve

BY S. FRANCIS, H. DUGMORE & RICO.

EVERYBODY!... I PROPOSE A TOAST!... TO THE **NEW SOUTH AFRICA!**

YES. MORE CHAMPAGNE OVER HERE!

I HATE MADAM'S FANCY DRESS PARTIES.

EVE! GIVE THE **PIG** AND THE **COW** SOME MORE CHAMPAGNE...

YES, MADAM.

...BUT DON'T GIVE ANY TO THE **HORSE**. HE'S HAD TOO MUCH ALREADY..

ATTENTION EVERYONE! I WISH TO MAKE A SPEECH!

SSHH!

SHH.

YOU KNOW WHAT'S **SO** BEAUTIFUL? UNDER ALL THESE COSTUMES, YOU CAN'T TELL IF WE'RE **BLACK** OR **WHITE**...

EXACTLY! IT PROVES THAT PEOPLE OF DIFFERENT CULTURES AND RACIAL BACK-GROUNDS CAN... CAN..

RIGHT! THERE'S A MORAL LESSON HERE, BUT I'M NOT SURE WHAT IT IS...

HEAR, HEAR!

OINK! OINK!

© Rapid Phase Entertainment 1992

MOOO! MOOO!

HEE-HAW!

OINK OINK!

CAW-CAW!

BAA BAAA!

GREAT... THAT'S ALL THE NEW SOUTH AFRICA NEEDS... **BARNYARD LIBERALS.**

OINK-OINK!

CAW CAW!

MADAM & Eve

BY S. FRANCIS, H. DUGMORE & RICO

EVE...HAVE I TOLD YOU RECENTLY HOW MUCH I **APPRECIATE** YOU?

SHE'S BEEN DRINKING SHERRY AGAIN.

REALLY. I JUST DON'T KNOW WHAT I'D DO WITHOUT YOU!

YEP. DEFINITELY THE SHERRY.

I MEAN IT'S **AMAZING**. AFTER ALL THIS TIME TOGETHER, I THINK WE'VE COME TO A SHARED AND COMMON **UNDERSTANDING**.

YES, I DO ALL THE WORK.

AND I ALWAYS TRY TO BE FAIR. IF YOU **EVER** HAVE A PROBLEM... YOU KNOW WHERE TO FIND ME.

SURE. IN FRONT OF THE T.V.

...AFTER ALL THESE YEARS, I WOULD SAY I KNOW ALL THERE IS TO KNOW ABOUT YOU!

...EXCEPT FOR MY SURNAME...

AFTER ALL, YOU SEEM TO REALLY **ENJOY** YOUR WORK.

...ABOUT AS MUCH AS GOING TO THE DENTIST...

YES EVE...I KNOW **EVERYTHING** ABOUT YOU! IN FACT... I'LL BET YOU **FIVE RAND** I CAN TELL YOU **EXACTLY** WHAT YOU'RE **THINKING** RIGHT NOW.

YOU'RE ON.

YOU'RE THINKING...I'M BOORISH, INSENSITIVE, AND I DON'T KNOW WHAT THE HELL I'M TALKING ABOUT.

...WELL?

...DO YOU HAVE CHANGE FOR A TWENTY?

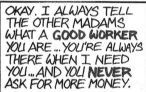

WELL SOL... WE'RE ALL ALONE AND MADAM'S GONE TO BED

GREAT! LET'S SEE WHAT'S ON **TV**!

...AND NOW BACK TO TONIGHT'S MOVIE..."INVASION OF THE SLIME CREATURES"

ALL RIGHT! A HORROR FILM.

I DON'T LIKE THESE STORIES, SOL. THEY **SCARE** ME.

TAKE IT EASY, EVE. IT'S ONLY A MOVIE.

WHAT WAS THAT? I HEARD SOMETHING AT THE DOOR!

MAYBE IT WAS JUST THE WIND.

© Rapid Phase Entertainment 1993

GASP! IT'S A MONSTER! ...WITH **SIX EYES** AND COVERED WITH **GREEN SLIME**!

STAY BACK! DON'T COME ANY CLOSER! NO! AAAAAH! **CRUNCH! CRUNCH! MUNCH!**

WHERE'RE YOU GOING?!

WILL YOU **RELAX**? I'M GETTING SOME POPCORN.

AAAAAAH!

COULD YOU TURN DOWN THE TV? I'M TRYING TO SLEEP.

SOL! ARE YOU ALL RIGHT?!

...A MINUTE... JUST GIVE ME A MINUTE...

MORNING MADAM. CAN I HAVE A RAISE?

IT'S MY MAID, DOCTOR. JUST BECAUSE I WON'T GIVE HER A PAY INCREASE-- SHE'S HAUNTING ME!

"HAUNTING YOU"?

YES! HAUNTING ME!! EVERYWHERE I GO, I SEE HER FACE!

AT RESTAURANTS...

CAN I TAKE YOUR ORDER?

...AT THE SUPERMARKET...

...EVEN IN MUSEUMS!

YOU'VE GOT TO HELP ME, DOCTOR! I DON'T KNOW WHAT TO DO!

WELL, IF IT BOTHERS YOU THAT MUCH...

...WHY NOT JUST GIVE YOUR MAID A RAISE?

WAIT! COME BACK! YOU STILL HAVE TEN MINUTES LEFT!

68

MADAM & Eve

BY S. FRANCIS, H. DUGMORE & RICO.

HELLO. THIS IS DANIE DU TOIT, CEO OF TELKOM. LATELY I'VE BEEN BEGGING YOUR FORGIVENESS FOR OUR TERRIBLE TELEPHONE SERVICE IN A SERIES OF **CLOYING TV ADVERTS**... •

...BUT SO FAR, NOBODY'S BUYING IT.

YOU CAN SAY **THAT** AGAIN, DANIE!

I'VE TRIED **EVERYTHING**... BEGGING... PLEADING... HUMBLE SINCERITY... EVEN MAUDLIN VIOLIN MUSIC -- BUT SO FAR, **NOTHING WORKS!!**

I MEAN, HOW MANY TIMES MUST I **APOLOGISE** BEFORE YOU FORGIVE US ?!!

AND SO... AFTER MANY EMOTIONAL MEETINGS WITH OUR PUBLIC RELATIONS CONSULTANTS, WE HERE AT TELKOM HAVE COME UP WITH A **FINAL SOLUTION**.

AS YOU CAN SEE, I AM NOW HOLDING A LOADED **.45 HANDGUN** TO MY HEAD, AND I WILL PULL THE TRIGGER IN **EXACTLY** SIXTY SECONDS...

ONLY **YOU**, THE **CONSUMER**, CAN **SAVE** ME... BY DIALLING OUR SPECIAL TOLL-FREE "I FORGIVE TELKOM" NUMBER AT THE BOTTOM OF YOUR SCREEN. MY FATE IS IN YOUR HANDS...

FIFTY-NINE... FIFTY-EIGHT... FIFTY-SEVEN...

QUICK EVE! **HELP HIM!!**

: CHOKE : PLEASE... ISN'T THERE **ANYONE** OUT THERE WHO FORGIVES US ?!!

BLAM! ...THUD!

...THE PHONE'S OUT OF ORDER.

© Rapid Phase Entertainment 1993

73

© Rapid Phase Entertainment 1993

FOR **YEARS**, WHITE PEOPLE EVERYWHERE HAVE OFTEN WONDERED WHAT GOES ON INSIDE A **MAID'S** LIVING QUARTERS...

AND **TONIGHT**... THANKS TO EVE SISULU, OUR CAMERAS WILL ACTUALLY **GO BEHIND** THE DOOR AND EXPOSE THE SHOCKING SECRETS OF A TYPICAL MAID'S ROOM...

EVE -- I UNDERSTAND EVERY MAID TAKES AN **OATH** NEVER TO ALLOW THEIR MADAMS INSIDE.

YES, GILLIAN. BUT **YOU'RE** PAYING ME A **LOT** OF MONEY.

... AND WE'LL BE OPENING THE DOOR RIGHT AFTER THIS BRIEF MESSAGE...

HURRY UP!!

AND NOW, FOR THE FIRST TIME ANYWHERE, WHITE SOUTH AFRICANS WILL ACTUALLY **SEE** THE INSIDE OF A REAL MAID'S LIVING QUARTERS.

EVE... IS IT ALMOST... **YES! THE DOOR IS OPEN!** WE'RE GOING **INSIDE!**

EVE -- WHAT ARE THESE HUGE **PILES** ON THE FLOOR?

COFFEE AND SUGAR, GILLIAN. I'VE BEEN STEALING A LITTLE EACH WEEK SINCE 1975.

I KNEW IT! I KNEW IT!

LET'S CONTINUE TO EXPLORE THE SECRETS INSIDE A TYPICAL MAID'S LIVING QUARTERS...

SO EVE... YOU'VE BEEN STEALING YOUR MADAM'S COFFEE AND SUGAR SINCE 1975?

WOULD YOU LIKE A CUP? 1983 WAS A VERY GOOD YEAR.

...WHAT ELSE DO YOU STEAL?

MOSTLY BELTS AND SOCKS. MADAM GOES **CRAZY** TRYING TO FIND THEM.

CHUCKLE ...SHE SPENT A WHOLE WEEK LOOKING FOR **THIS** ONE.

HEY! MY RED BELT!!

MADAM & Eve

BY S. FRANCIS, H. DUGMORE & RICO.

Panel 1:
HI MOM. AM I INTERRUPTING ANYTHING?

ACTUALLY, YOU ARE, ERIC. IT'S OUR "**MADAM-MAID QUALITY TIME**."

Panel 2:
QUALITY TIME?!

DON'T WORRY. I'M GETTING **PAID** FOR IT.

Panel 3:
OKAY EVE, FOR TODAY'S "MADAM-MAID QUALITY TIME", I'M GOING TO TEACH YOU HOW TO PLAY CHESS.

Panel 4:
FIRST OF ALL, YOU'VE GOT TO KNOW ALL THE PIECES. THERE'S A **KING** ...THERE'S A **BISHOP** AND THERE'S LOTS OF **PAWNS** ...

Panel 5:
SO FAR, I LIKE THIS GAME. IT REMINDS ME OF SOUTH AFRICA.

Panel 6:
OKAY. GO AHEAD, EVE. IT'S YOUR MOVE.

Panel 7:
NO, NO, NO, EVE! THAT IS **MY** PIECE YOU JUST MOVED. I'M **BLACK** AND YOU'RE **WHITE**!

© Rapid Phase Entertainment 1993

Panel 8:
...PAY ATTENTION, EVE. REMEMBER, I'M **BLACK** AND YOU'RE **WHITE**.

Panel 9:
YOU'RE BLACK AND I'M WHITE. GOT IT.

Panel 10:
...THINGS ARE GETTING REALLY **CONFUSING** IN THE NEW SOUTH AFRICA.

MADAM & Eve

BY S. FRANCIS, H. DUGMORE & RICO.

HI. DANIE DU TOIT, PROUD HEAD OF **TELKOM**. I'M GOING DOOR 'TO DOOR TO MEET EACH AND EVERY TELKOM CUSTOMER.

COULD I HAVE AN HOUR OF YOUR TIME?

AAAAAAH!!

YOU SEE, OUR PUBLIC RELATIONS PEOPLE SUGGESTED I GET OUT THERE AND **PERSONALLY** RE-STORE CONFIDENCE IN OUR TROUBLED TELEPHONE SYSTEM.

OF COURSE, YOU'RE PROBABLY SAYING "HEY DANIE -- INSTEAD OF SPENDING **MILLIONS** ON ADVERTISING, WHY NOT JUST IMPROVE THE SERVICE ?!"

BUT DID YOU KNOW THAT RE-CENTLY, TELKOM'S HEAD OFFICE RECEIVED THOUSANDS OF LETTERS AND **NOT ONE OF THEM WAS NEGATIVE** ?!!

BUT MR. DU TOIT-- THOSE LETTERS WERE WRITTEN BY YOUR **OWN EMPLOYEES** !!

PLEASE. CALL ME DANIE.

OKAY. LET ME GET TO THE POINT. I'M **NOT LEAVING** YOUR HOUSE UNTIL YOU **ADMIT** THE PHONE SERVICE HAS IMPROVED AND YOU PLEDGE YOUR **UNDYING LOYALTY** TO TELKOM.

WHAT?! THIS IS **BLACKMAIL!**-- I REFUSE !!

LET ME ASK YOUR MAID. HAS OUR SERVICE IMPROVED?

I WOULDN'T KNOW. MA-DAM ALWAYS LOCKS THE TELEPHONE.

HELLO, PETE? DANIE. WE GOT A COUPLE OF **HOLD-OUTS** ON THE PLEDGE THING. I MIGHT HAVE TO STAY HERE FOR A FEW DAYS.

OKAY! **YOU WIN!** IN MY OPINION, YOUR SERVICE HAS **IMPROVED** TREMENDOUSLY !!

SORRY. I'M UN-CONVINCED. WHAT'S FOR DINNER?

MADAM & Eve

BY S. FRANCIS, H. DUGMORE & RICO.

LOOK MADAM! WE GOT A LETTER! LISTEN: "CONGRATULATIONS... YOU MAY HAVE **ALREADY WON** A NEW CAR, A CASH PRIZE, A LUXURY VACATION..."

"...OR A SEAT ON THE **NEW SABC BOARD**."

NEXT! NUMBER 743 AND 744!

THAT'S US! LET'S GO!

WELCOME TO THE SABC BOARD SELECTION PROCEEDINGS. DO YOU HAVE ANY QUESTIONS?

ACTUALLY, YES. WHY ARE WE HERE?

YOU'RE MADAM & EVE! WE FEEL THAT YOUR' WELL-KNOWN RACIAL HARMONY AND TOLERANCE MIGHT BRING A UNIQUE PERSPECTIVE TO THE SABC.

OKAY. MY FIRST SUGGESTION WOULD BE... **MORE** SOAP OPERAS AND LESS OF THOSE TEDIOUS BLACK LANGUAGE PROGRAMS.

© Rapid Phase Entertainment 1993

WAIT A MINUTE! I **LIKE** THOSE SHOWS!!

WELL, MAYBE YOU SHOULD BE **WORKING** MORE INSTEAD OF WATCHING TELEVISION!

HA! **YOU** SHOULD TALK! **ALL** YOU DO IS SIT IN FRONT OF THE **TV!**

I CAN DO WHAT I WANT! IT'S **MY** HOUSE!

AND I'M THE ONE WHO CLEANS IT!

OKAY. I THINK WE'RE DONE HERE.

I GUESS THIS MEANS WE DIDN'T WIN THE CAR.

NEXT! NUMBER 746... ABDUL BHAMJEE.

90

MADAM & Eve

BY S. FRANCIS, H. DUGMORE & RICO.

IT WAS NICE OF YOU TO ASK US FOR DINNER, MOM. YOU'RE HANDLING THIS VERY WELL.

NO PROBLEM! ...MY SON UNEXPECTEDLY BRINGS HOME HIS NEW BLACK GIRLFRIEND FROM UNIVERSITY... IT'S THE LEAST I COULD DO!!

Eric... She's eating her soup with a fork.

I know. ...Just keep smiling.

SO, HOW'D THE TWO OF YOU MEET?

ACTUALLY, IN JAIL.

WE WERE ARRESTED TOGETHER DURING A STUDENT PROTEST MARCH.

WOULD YOU EXCUSE ME? I HAVE TO CHECK ON THE REST OF THE FOOD.

EVE! YOU'VE GOT TO HELP ME! I CAN'T HANDLE THIS!

NONSENSE, MADAM. YOU'RE DOING FINE.

I'M A MESS! I DON'T KNOW WHAT TO DO! I DON'T KNOW WHAT TO SAY!

YOU CAN DO IT, MADAM! JUST GO OUT THERE AND MAKE SMALL TALK!

© Rapid Phase Entertainment · 1993

SO.

ERIC... YOUR GIRLFRIEND HAS SUCH A PRETTY NAME. "LIZEKA" ...IT'S VERY UNIQUE.

I KNOW. IN ZULU IT MEANS... "SHE WHO BEARS MANY CHILDREN QUICKLY."

W--Water---

CHEW SLOWER, MOM.

93

HI, WE'RE MADAM & EVE. JOIN US FOR THE THIRD THRILLING INSTALMENT OF...

101 USES FOR A NEW CONSTITUTION

USE #73: FIX THAT WOBBLY TABLE ONCE AND FOR ALL...

USE #38: FOOL YOUR TEACHER OR PROFESSOR...

USE #59: PROTECT CHURCHES, SYNAGOGUES, MOSQUES AND TEMPLES ACROSS THE COUNTRY...

SOUTH AFRICA'S NEW CONSTITUTION IS FAIR TO EVERYONE! EVE TELLS ME IT PROVIDES FOR EXTENDED, TWO-HOUR LUNCH-BREAKS FOR MAIDS ON TUESDAYS, THURSDAYS AND SATURDAYS...

NICE TRY, EVE!!

DARN.

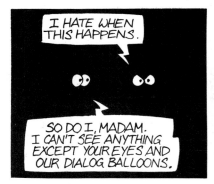

MADAM & Eve

BY S. FRANCIS, H. DUGMORE & RICO.

GOOD MORNING SOUTH AFRICA! TODAY THE MP'S OF THE CP AND NP AGREED TO TEA WITH THE ANC TO DISCUSS THE IFP, THE PAC, AND TO SEE IF THE SPCA IS A FRONT FOR THE AWB, THE CIA AND THE KGB. THIS IS GMSA. STAY TUNED FOR UB-40 BROUGHT TO YOU BY CNA AND OK...

EVE! I NEED MORE COFFEE!

WHAT'S WRONG, MADAM?

I'LL TELL YOU WHAT'S **WRONG!** IT'S THIS **COUNTRY.** IT'S GETTING SO **CONFUSING!** YOU CAN'T TELL WHAT'S GOING ON ANY MORE!

ACTUALLY--POLITICALLY SPEAKING--IT'S VERY SIMPLE. IS THERE ANYTHING I CAN HELP YOU UNDERSTAND?

OKAY-- **MISS SMARTY PANTS** -- EXPLAIN TO ME.

WHAT'S HAPPENING ARE PREDICTABLE MANIFESTATIONS OF CONTRADICTIONS BETWEEN A MULTI-ETHNIC SOCIAL PLURALITY AND A UNITARY ECONOMIC SYSTEM.

IN SHORT, THE CHALLENGE IS TO FORGE A HUMANE COALITION OF MINIMALLY SHARED VALUES AND THUS PREVENT BASE-SUPERSTRUCTURE CLEAVAGES FROM RENDING OUR NATION ASUNDER.

...YOU'RE FIRED.

CALL ME WHEN YOU FINISH YOUR COFFEE.

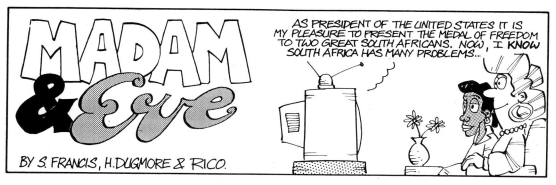

MADAM & Eve

BY S. FRANCIS, H. DUGMORE & RICO.

AS PRESIDENT OF THE UNITED STATES IT IS MY PLEASURE TO PRESENT THE MEDAL OF FREEDOM TO TWO GREAT SOUTH AFRICANS. NOW, I KNOW SOUTH AFRICA HAS MANY PROBLEMS...

...AT A RECENT PARTY AT BARBRA STREISAND'S HOUSE, WHOOPI GOLDBERG TOLD ME ALL ABOUT THEM.

ALSO, IN OTHER CONVERSATIONS WITH PAUL SIMON AND LOU GOSSET JR.--

UH, SIR? WE'RE LEAVING FOR JAPAN IN 45 MINUTES.

WHAT? OH. RIGHT. ...WITHOUT FURTHER ADO, LET ME INTRODUCE TWO WONDERFUL GUYS...

YOU'VE SEEN THEM ON THE COVERS OF TIME AND NEWSWEEK... ...AND ONE OF THEM WAS EVEN IN "MALCOLM X"-- A MAJOR HOLLYWOOD RELEASE--

PLEASE WELCOME... FW DE KLERK...AND NELSON MANDELA!

CLAP CLAP CLAP CLAP CLAP CLAP CLAP. CLAP CLAP

MR. MANDELA, MR. DE KLERK -- I'M PROUD TO PRESENT YOU WITH THESE MEDALS...FOR YOUR JOINT EFFORT TOWARD PEACE, EQUALITY AND UNITY

HEY! HIS MEDAL IS BIGGER THAN MINE!

IT IS NOT!!

© Rapid Phase Entertainment 1993

GENTLEMEN... I ASSURE YOU... BOTH MEDALS ARE EXACTLY THE SAME.

FINE! THEN NOBODY SHOULD MIND IF WE TRADE!

HEY! LET GO OF MY MEDAL! MR PRESIDENT! HE TOOK MY MEDAL!

GENTLEMEN, PLEASE! THIS IS A SOLEMN OCCASION!

WELL, HE STARTED IT!

DID NOT! DID NOT!

DID TOO! DID TOO!

DID NOT! DID NOT!

OKAY, YOU TWO! WE **KNOW** YOU'RE **IN** THERE! WE'RE COMING IN!!

IS IT THE POLICE!?

NO! THE ANC FUNDRAISING COMITTEE!

BEFORE YOU SAY ANYTHING -- I'M NOT MAKING **ANY** DONATIONS TO POLITICAL PARTIES.

DID WE **ASK** FOR DONATIONS?

HEY--WE DON'T EXPECT SOMETHING FOR NOTHING. HERE -- CHECK THIS OUT.

ANC SCRATCH 'N WIN CARDS! WIN **BIG PRIZES** OF CASH AND MERCHANDISE!

NOT INTERESTED.

FINE. HOW ABOUT THIS? JOIN THE **ANC CLUB!** FOR A HUNDRED BUCKS, **YOU** GET A HAT, A T-SHIRT...

FORGET IT.

OKAY. I CAN SEE YOU'RE A TOUGH CUSTOMER. HERE'S THE PIÈCE DE RESISTANCE! OUR **MOST** POPULAR ITEM! FOR ONLY **200 BUCKS**, YOU CAN HAVE YOUR PICTURE TAKEN WITH... NELSON MANDELA!

© Rapid Phase Entertainment - 1993

I CAN'T BELIEVE IT! IS THE ANC **THAT** DESPERATE FOR MONEY--GOING **DOOR TO DOOR** AND CHARGING 200 RAND FOR A PHOTO-GRAPH WITH A LIFESIZE **MANDELA CARDBOARD CUT-OUT**!?

...CARDBOARD CUT-OUT? WHO SAID ANYTHING ABOUT A CARDBOARD CUT-OUT?

DID YOU CLOSE THE DEAL? IT'S COLD OUT HERE.

ALMOST, SIR. STAND BY.

MADAM & Eve

BY S. FRANCIS, H. DUGMORE & RICO.

MADAM -- I KNOW YOUR MOTHER CAME ALL THE WAY FROM **ENGLAND** TO VISIT YOU IN SOUTH AFRICA... *BUT SHE'S DRIVING ME CRAZY!!*

SHE'S JUST STAYING FOR A WEEK. HOW HARD CAN IT BE?

YOU CALL THIS HOUSE **CLEAN**? IN MY HOUSE YOU CAN **EAT** OFF THE FLOOR!

EVE! SHE'S OVER EIGHTY!!

NOW, I WANT YOU TWO TO GET TO KNOW EACH OTHER. YOU PROBABLY HAVE A LOT IN COMMON.

BACK IN ENGLAND THERE'S A BOY NAMED LEROY WHO DELIVERS MY GROCERIES. HE'S **ALSO** BLACK. DO YOU KNOW HIM?

NO.

SO. HOW MUCH DOES MY DAUGHTER **PAY** YOU?

I'M NOT SURE. I SPEND ALL THE MONEY ON BRANDY AND MEN.

I KNEW IT! WHAT TYPE OF FOOD DO YOU AFRICANS EAT?

WHATEVER I **CATCH**, I COOK.

I HEAR YOU PEOPLE HAVE LOTS OF **VIOLENCE** IN THIS COUNTRY.

ACTUALLY, IT'S NOT REAL.' IT'S AN **ACT** WE DO FOR THE TOURISTS AND TV-CAMERAS.

SO. DO YOU HAVE ANY HOBBIES?

...HAVE YOU EVER HEARD OF **SHRUNKEN HEADS**?

EVE! I'M LISTENING TO THIS!!

108

MADAM & Eve

BY S. FRANCIS, H. DUGMORE & RICO.

MADAM--THIS IS MY FRIEND **DR. CHILL**, FROM GRAHAMSTOWN. HE'S A VERY TALENTED ANGRY YOUNG POET.

YO! VAPORISE THE VOID - CAUTERIZE THE CHOLESTEROL - AND PLUNGE INTO THE HEART OF WHITENESS!!

...HE SAYS... "HELLO."

HE TALKS PRETTY **LOUD**, DOESN'T HE?

ACTUALLY, HE'S PARTIALLY **DEAF**. BEFORE HE BECAME A PEOPLE'S POET, HE WAS A REVOLUTIONARY. UNFORTUNATELY A **BOMB** EXPLODED BY HIS EAR.

SHAME. HOW DID IT HAPPEN?

HE FORGOT TO SET THE TIMER.

WHAT!?

DON'T WORRY, MADAM. HE'S **FAMOUS** NOW! HIS ONE-MAN SHOW AT THE GRAHAMSTOWN FESTIVAL WAS COMPLETELY SOLD OUT!

GWEN! THERE'S A **STRANGE BLACK MAN** IN THE HOUSE!!

UH-OH.

WHO ARE YOU?

© Rapid Phase Entertainment. 1993

ACCESSORIZE AND MOBILISE BEFORE IT'S TOO LATE!

BONK!

MOM!!

THAT'S HOW WE DEAL WITH RUDE PEOPLE IN ENGLAND.

...LAST TIME I BRING A **CELEBRITY** TO THIS HOUSE!

112

MADAM & EVE

BY S. FRANCIS, H. DUGMORE & RICO.

OUR TOP STORY... **MICHAEL JACKSON** ARRIVED IN SOUTH AFRICA TODAY TO **PERSONALLY** APPROVE THE VENUES FOR HIS FUTURE CONCERTS. THE SUPERSTAR HAS REFUSED ALL INTERVIEWS... AND WHERE JACKSON AND HIS ENTOURAGE ARE **SECRETLY STAYING** WHILE IN SOUTH AFRICA, IS A MYSTERY.

OKAY MEN... CAREFUL WITH THAT OXYGEN BED!

EXCUSE ME... MR. BODYGUARD?

WHAT?

WHY **US**? OUT OF **ALL** THE PEOPLE IN SOUTH AFRICA, WHY DID MICHAEL JACKSON DECIDE TO STAY WITH US?

OUR INVESTIGATIONS SHOWED THAT YOU AND EVE ARE A **POSITIVE** REFLECTION OF A CHANGING SOUTH AFRICA.

REALLY?

YES. THAT, AND THE FACT THAT ELIZABETH TAYLOR LIKES YOUR STRIP. BY THE WAY-- WE'LL BE PUTTING HER SHRINE IN THE DINING ROOM.

HE'S ARRIVED, SIR.

RIGHT.

MICHAEL... MAY I PRESENT MADAM & EVE -- YOUR HOSTS IN SOUTH AFRICA.

OUR PLEASURE, MR. JACK-SON.

HEAL THE WORLD. HEAL THE CHILDREN.

...HE REALLY **LIKES** YOU. I CAN TELL.

...HE LOOKS A LOT **WHITER** THAN I EXPECTED.

EVE!! THERE'S A CHIMPANZEE IN MY BATHROOM!!

© Rapid Phase Entertainment 1993

...AND TODAY'S TOP NEWS STORY... **MICHAEL JACKSON** ARRIVED IN SOUTH AFRICA TODAY TO PERSONALLY APPROVE THE SITES OF HIS FUTURE CONCERTS...

DECLINING ALL INTER-VIEWS, MANAGERS FOR THE 'SUPERSTAR' REFUSE TO DIVULGE **WHERE** MICHAEL IS SECRETLY STAYING...

...ALTHOUGH IT IS **RUMOURED** THAT JACKSON AND HIS ENTOURAGE SELECTED A PRIVATE RESIDENCE SOMEWHERE IN JOHANNESBURG ---

SO. WHAT'S ELIZABETH TAYLOR **REALLY** LIKE?

VERY SENSITIVE. WE SHARE THE SAME HAIRDRESSER.

MARGE -- I REALLY CAN'T TALK LONG ... BUT YOU'VE GOT TO **PROMISE** NOT TO REPEAT THIS ...

I CAN'T BELIEVE IT !! WHILE HE'S HERE IN SOUTH AFRICA, **MICHAEL JACKSON** IS STAYING AT **OUR** HOUSE !!

NO!!

IT'S THE TRUTH ! HE'S IN THE LOUNGE **RIGHT NOW** WITH EVE ! THEY'RE DISCUSSING RACISM AND SOUTH AFRICAN POLITICS!

NO KIDDING! ONLY **THREE** TIMES?

NOSE, CHIN AND CHEEKBONES. THAT'S IT.

I CAN'T BELIEVE WE'RE SITTING IN OUR **OWN** HOUSE TALKING TO MICHAEL JACKSON !

MICHAEL... WHAT DO YOU THINK OF SOUTH AFRICA'S RACIAL PROBLEMS?

LIKE THE EBONY AND IVORY KEYS ON A PIANO, YOU SHOULD ALL LIVE TOGETHER IN HARMONY.

SO... YOU'RE NOT **NERVOUS** ABOUT BEING IN A COUNTRY WITH A HISTORY OF APARTHEID ?

NOT REALLY...

OF COURSE, I'M A **WHITE** MAN NOW.

GOOD POINT.

MADAM & Eve

BY S. FRANCIS, H. DUGMORE & RICO.

BUT MADAM-- I **HATE** NEW YEAR'S RESOLUTIONS.

THIS TIME, WE'LL MAKE IT FUN! I'LL WRITE A LIST FOR **YOU**... AND YOU WRITE A LIST OF NEW YEAR'S RESOLUTIONS FOR **ME**.

...BETTER GIVE ME SEVERAL SHEETS OF PAPER.

ARE YOU SURE YOU DON'T WANT TO STOP AND **REST** YOUR HAND?

NO... I'M FINE.

OKAY! HOLD IT RIGHT THERE! LET ME SEE THAT LIST!

"GIVE EVE A **RAISE**." "BE NICER TO EVE." "GIVE EVE MORE **TIME OFF**."

ARE YOU CRAZY!?

MAY I CALL YOUR ATTENTION TO NUMBER 28.

"LEARN TO ACCEPT EVE'S CRITICISM GRACIOUSLY AND STOP **YELLING** SO MUCH."

HEY--YOU ASKED FOR MY INPUT.

THAT'S THE LAST TIME I TRY TO HELP **YOU** BECOME A BETTER PERSON!!

MADAM & EVE

BY S. FRANCIS, H. DUGMORE & RICO.

Twas the night before Christmas And all through the house...

Not a creature could enter. Not even a mouse...

FIRST STRIKE SECURITY & ARMED RESPONSE

Father Christmas arrived as the hour grew late. Accidentally he touched an electrified gate.

BZAARP!

He tried the barred windows and stuck through his arm...

Setting off an expensive but silent alarm.

"I'll get in through the chimney! I'm not beaten yet!"

...But the chimney was blocked-- CCV and M-Net.

His glove touched the wall set with glass and sharp nail...

Then Armed Response Guards came to take him to jail.

FREEZE, SUCKER!

"Hey!" said the Madam-"Stop acting so tough!" "It's Father Christmas!" said Eve. "Now take off those cuffs!"

© Rapid Phase Entertainment 1992

Then the Madam and Maid gave him food and a drink.

And they washed all his wounds in the large kitchen sink.

"If it wasn't for us... if we didn't care..." "He might've **"slipped in the shower"** at John Vorster Square!"

And they heard him exclaim as he drove out of sight... "MERRY CHRISTMAS TO ALL! AND TO ALL A GOOD NIGHT!"